# Pattern Blocks Activities B

Marian Pasternack
Linda Silvey

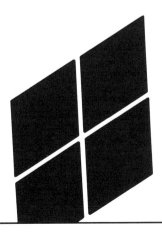

Creative Publications

Line drawings by the authors.

Cover design by JoAnne Hammer

©1975 Creative Publications
788 Palomar Avenue
Sunnyvale, CA 94086
Printed in U.S.A.

ISBN: 0-88488-042-7


13  14  15.  9 5 4 3 2 1 0 8 9

# Table of Contents

# Introduction

*Pattern Block Activities* books A and B contain classroom-tested activity sheets to use to teach mathematics with pattern blocks. Book A is designed for grades 2-6; book B is appropriate for grades 4-9. However, older students who are unfamiliar with pattern blocks may find that many of the worksheets in the first book serve as a good introduction to topics in the second book.

Activities in both books involve concepts of operations, measurement, geometry, relations and functions, problem solving, and logical thinking. Each volume includes patterns to complete. Although the instructions on the activity pages are directed to the student, students need not be able to read them; they are there to aid the teacher. The section in "Directions and Extensions," following this introduction, is additional teacher guidance.

Most students enjoy working with pattern blocks which help them develop an intuitive understanding of aspects of mathematics. As with any new tool, it is important to have sufficient "free play" to become familiar with the pieces. The amount of free play each child needs will vary. We hope that all children will have a chance to explore relationships, identify pieces, and make designs before they are presented with written materials created by someone else.

Once students are familiar with the blocks it may be helpful to discuss the geometric names. On the activity sheets, pieces are identified by proper name and color. A discussion of these terms may avoid future confusion.

These books contain a limited number of activities for each concept explored. For some children these will be ample and after completing them the students will be anxious to go on by themselves. We hope they will be given that privilege. For other students, the activities in the books are too few to develop an understanding of the concept. We hope that when this happens the teacher will develop additional worksheets to help the child reap the full benefit from these manipulative materials.

Each page is perforated so that it can be conveniently torn out and placed in a plastic activity card sleeve, or used as a duplicating master to make copies for individuals or small groups.

These activity pages can be used in a variety of classroom settings. They can be used in a lab situation where the teacher introduces the task and children work independently with the blocks. As a math class activity, the teacher can introduce a task to a small group and have the students work together. In a more directed group situation, a teacher may introduce the task and work through it with the class. A student who has already successfully completed the task may act as a group leader or help students who are having difficulty. Teachers should select appropriate pages for their classes and allot the proper amount of time for each lesson. Some pages can be completed in a class period while others need more time.

Student progress can be evaluated in several ways. If students work in pairs or small groups the teacher can learn a lot from circulating among the groups and listening to the conversation. If children are working independently, they can be encouraged to record their work using pattern block stickers, available from Creative Publications, or tracing and coloring their patterns. These records make attractive display papers. Solutions are listed in a section following the activity sheets to aid in evaluation of student comprehension.

Young students may have difficulty perceiving the transformations of blocks that have been flipped or rotated. This will be evident if the child inaccurately places the blocks on the page. In this case, the teacher may wish to develop a set of cards to provide practice rearranging the blocks. More advanced students will be interested in using the blocks to prove their answers. Discussion of proof in this manner is valuable.

These activities are designed to entertain as well as instruct. We hope you find the materials informative and enjoyable.

i

# Directions and Extensions

Students should become familiar with the relationships of various pattern blocks by illustrating equivalences.

*Extensions.* Students can create a pattern using a combination of blocks and give it to a friend to construct using a combination of different blocks.

The student should define number relationships of blocks using the hexagon as one whole.

*Extensions.* Use another block as one whole and redefine the number relationships of the blocks.

The student should find all of the combinations of blocks that represent the specified fractional parts of a hexagon.

*Extensions.* Find other fractional parts of a hexagon. Repeat these activities using different blocks to represent one. Hold contests to find specified fractional equivalents.

Students should construct the tree with blocks and then appropriately color the fraction parts written beside each hexagon.

*Extensions.* Have students use the blocks to build other designs that show fraction relationships. Have students work in pairs, one drawing a design that illustrates a fraction relationship and the other student appropriately coloring the design.

Students should use the specified blocks to build the changed orientation of the pattern and then record their answers by tracing the blocks. Several answers are possible for each pattern. Any combination of blocks is acceptable as long as the students' logic is sound.

*Extensions.* Students can make up their own patterns to use as activity sheets like these. Children may want to form small groups and work together developing patterns and directional changes for other small groups to work on. Be sure the answers are recorded by the designing group before the puzzle is presented to another group so that answers can be compared.

The student is to find the missing blocks in a ratio problem and record the answer by tracing the blocks. Children should record the numerical relationships involved in the ratio in the blanks provided.

*Extensions.* Students can make similar activity sheets and exchange them with friends. Divide the class into teams; give duplicate activity sheets to each team and see which team can finish the problem first. Discuss the answers as a class.

Students should use the specified blocks to build the designated figures. After making each type of construction, students should complete the table that follows the construction page. Some students will be able to identify the rule for each pattern. Discuss these discoveries. Encourage enthusiastic students to write the rule using symbols representing unknowns, such as a □ or a △.

*Extensions.* Students can develop other patterns with the blocks, record the pattern, and find the rule. They may begin by making squares with squares, rhombi with rhombi, and finding which shapes they can build this way.

## Perimeter                                                            Pages 20-25

Students find the perimeter of a given figure and then go on to build figures with a specified perimeter. Children then build figures with the smallest and the largest perimeter a specific number of blocks will allow. This helps develop an intuitive understanding of the varying perimeters a figure of a given area may have.

*Extensions.* Students can build patterns that show the development from the smallest to the largest perimeter in figures with a constant area and record the patterns. Students can work in groups to find all of the possible perimeters of figures using a specified number of a certain block or all of the possible figures, using one kind of block, with a specified perimeter. See Extensions Appendix A, page 84.

## Area-perimeter relationships                                         Pages 26-38

Area is briefly explained to the student. The activities that follow require children to identify a pattern in the relationship of area and perimeter in the model and then follow that pattern to build larger figures. After the building page is a recording table for the student to complete. Some students will discover a rule to follow to complete the table.

It is important that students understand that it is the numbers associated with perimeter and area that are compared not the concepts of perimeter and area. Students should realize that perimeter and area are actually two different things. Sometimes the number associated with perimeter will be greater than that associated with area and vice versa.

*Extensions.* Build figures with different specified areas. Build other patterns and complete an area-perimeter relationship table for them.

Teachers with an understanding of first year algebra may wish to consult Seymour and Shedd, *Finite Differences* for similar pattern activities.
See Extension Appendix B, page 85.

## Angle measure                                                         Pages 39-42

Using the knowledge that a circle has 360°, students are asked to find the measure of angles of pattern block pieces. This involves finding how many of a certain angle cover the circle, or 360°, and then dividing by the appropriate number of angles. Then the student is asked to find the number of degrees in an angle formed by two pattern blocks placed together.

*Extensions.* Have students build designs that show angles made of vertices of several pattern blocks and then describe the angle measure. Ask students to share patterns and check each other. Build patterns that sequence the sizes of angles of the blocks. Build patterns with only 90°, 60°, or 270° angles. Place two mirrors at the vertex of a block and discuss what can be seen.
See Extension Appendix C, page 86.

## Symmetry                                                              Pages 43-49

After symmetry is discussed students are asked to find lines of symmetry in given patterns and show their understanding by recording their results.

*Extensions.* Students should build patterns with the blocks and record them to give to a friend. The friend should find and record the lines of symmetry in the new design. See who can find the greatest number of lines of symmetry in a given design.
See Extension Appendix D, page 87.

## Symmetry in designs

Students are to complete the pattern and find the number of lines of symmetry in the finished design.

*Extensions.* Have students build designs and record the lines of symmetry. Then have them trace part of the design and give it to a friend to complete with the given number of lines of symmetry. Use a given number of blocks to build patterns with a specified number of lines of symmetry. Find who can build the greatest number of different designs with a specified number of lines of symmetry.

## Polygons and congruence

After polygons are defined students are to distinguish polygons from other figures. Congruence is then defined and students are asked to identify congruent figures and congruent angles.

*Extensions.* Students can work in pairs, one child building a figure using one or two kinds of blocks and the other child building a congruent figure using different kinds of blocks. For example,

original figure          congruent figure

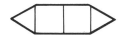 

Record these designs with pattern block stickers for pleasant classroom displays individually or combined to make a wall mosaic.

## Similarity

Similar figures are discussed and students are then asked to build some.

*Extensions.* Students can build similar designs with blocks and check each other for accuracy. Children enjoy building hexagons with two, three, and four unit edges. Graph paper is useful for drawing similar shapes and designs.

Have students test for similarity by projection. Hold a block well above a figure and move the block up and down until it is the same size as the figure on paper. If the two shapes look congruent this way, they are similar. Some pages in book B which show figures larger and similar to pattern block pieces are 17, 27, and 31.

## Regular polygons

Regular polygons are discussed in terms of symmetry.

*Extensions.* Students can outline other regular polygonal shapes and exchange drawings for friends to cover with blocks. Guide students to use compass, straight edge, and protractor to construct regular polygons. Teachers may wish to use Schadler and Seymour, *Creative Constructions* for this type of activity.
See Extension Appendix E, pages 88-90.

### Regular polygons
Pages 62-63

The students are asked to cover an outlined design using one kind of pattern block that is a regular polygon.

*Extensions.* Discuss what happens at vertices where polygons meet.

### Mosaic patterns
Pages 64-69

Lines of symmetry are discussed in relation to mosaic patterns as preparation for building activities that follow. In these, students are to build mosaic or repeating design patterns (tessellations) to cover an outlined shape, and then to extend the pattern. Children should be encouraged to notice the patterns formed at vertices where blocks meet and to use that pattern as a guide to extending the design.

*Extensions.* Find lines of symmetry in other combinations of blocks that tessellate (the patterned filling of space with no overlapping and no holes). Cut out any quadrilateral and see if it will tessellate. Then cut out any other identical nonregular polygonal shapes and find if they will tessellate. Investigate the patterns and tessellations in the artwork of M. C. Escher. Have students find and record complex wall or floor tiling patterns in buildings, magazines or catalogs. Have students find the patterned tessellations on pages 44-45, 47-49, and 52 of Silvey and Pasternack, *Pattern Blocks Coloring Book.*

### Naming tessellations
Pages 70-71

Students are introduced to a numerical notation for naming first regular and then semi-regular tessellations. Point out that this system is valid only for regular polygons because the number associated with the order of a polygon, for example 4 for a quadrilateral or a square, indicates that the polygon will be similar to others of the same numerical order.

*Extensions.* Find other regular and semi-regular tessellations in the book and name them. Draw patterns to record designs and describe them with numerical names. Have students work in pairs, one dictating a pattern, using numerical names, to the other who constructs the pattern with blocks.

### Dodecagon problems
Pages 72-83

The economy rule is explained and students are to use it in the activities that follow. When covering the dodecagons with blocks, any time a combination of blocks can be replaced with a single block the replacement must be made. The dodecagon covering activities provide practice following directions and solving problems.

*Extensions.* Students may enjoy competing to complete a specified dodecagon page and comparing results. Sometimes two children enjoy sitting back-to-back or with a barrier between them but close enough so that one child can choose a dodecagon from the page of 63 and describe the pattern to the other student who tries to construct it from the directions given. This can also be conducted as a small group activity.

How many of these:    Just cover these?

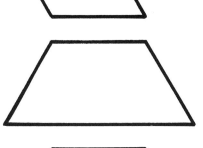

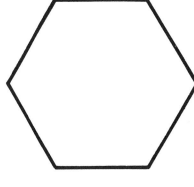

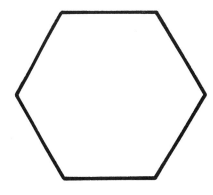

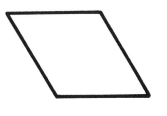

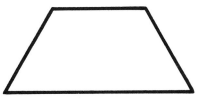
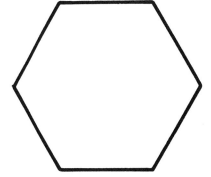

1

If the yellow hexagon is 1,

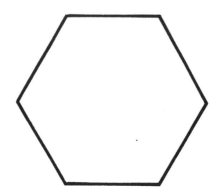

the red trapezoid is

 $\frac{1}{2}$ .

What is the
blue rhombus?

 _____

What is the
green triangle?

 _____

What are the
triangle and rhombus?

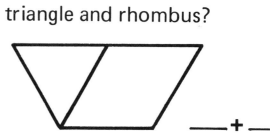 ___ **+** ___ **=** ___

What are the
rhombus and trapezoid?

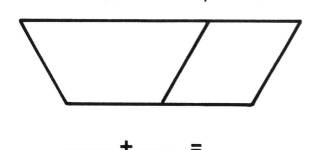

___ **+** ___ **=** ___

What are
two trapezoids?

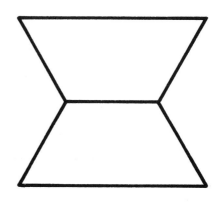

___ **+** ___ **=** ___

2

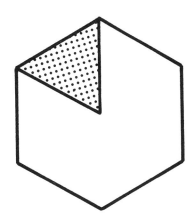

The area of the green triangle is $\frac{1}{6}$ the area of the yellow hexagon.

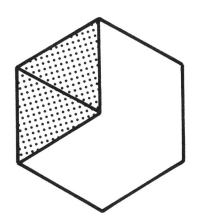 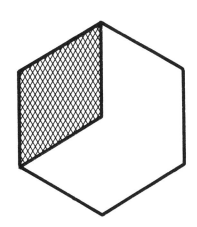

These show $\frac{2}{6}$.

Can you show $\frac{3}{6}$ three different ways?

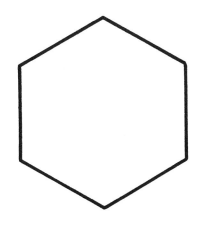 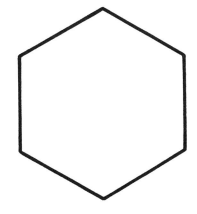 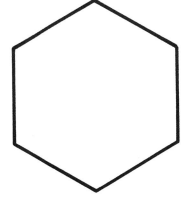

Can you find four *different* ways to show $\frac{4}{6}$?

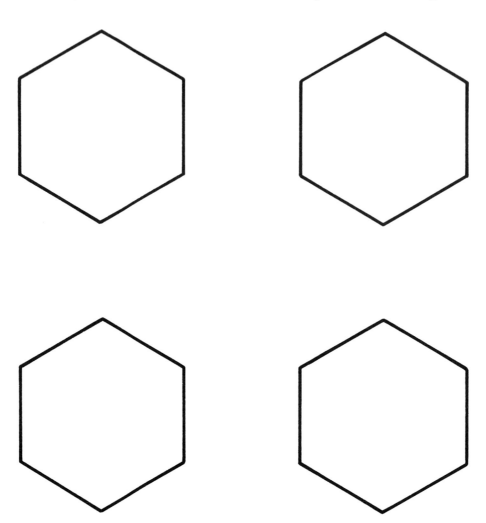

Can you find five *different* ways to show $\frac{5}{6}$?

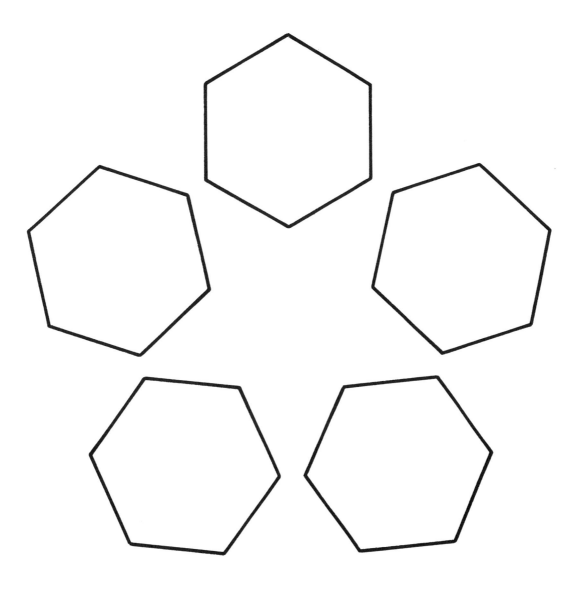

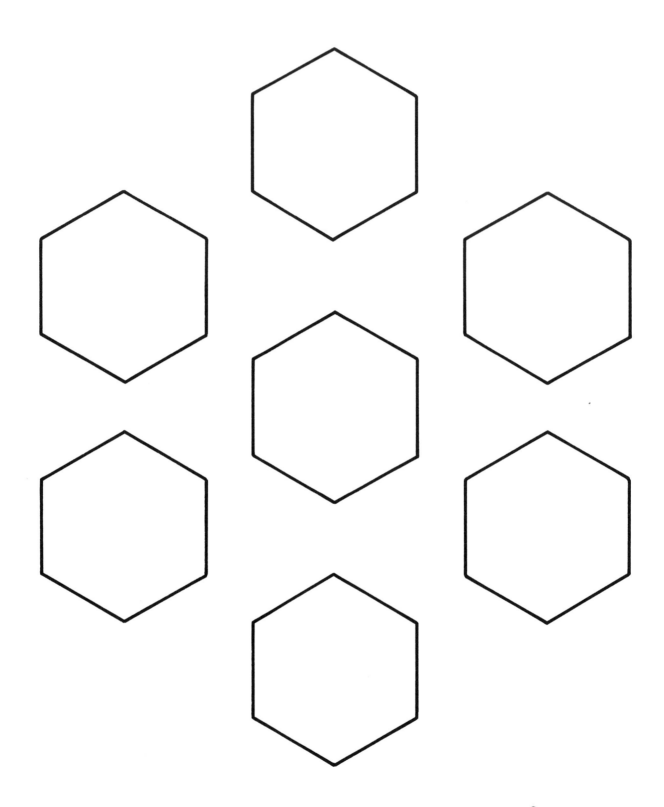

Can you find seven *different* ways  to show $\frac{6}{6}$?

Color the fraction tree.
What pattern can you find?

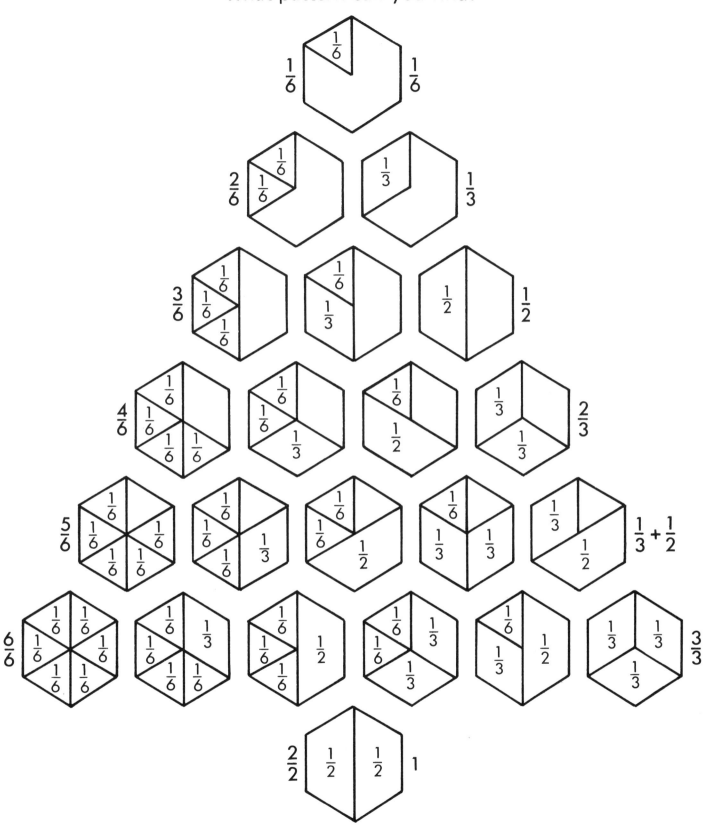

7

# Trace your answers.

This     is     to     this     as     this     is     to     this.
Sample:

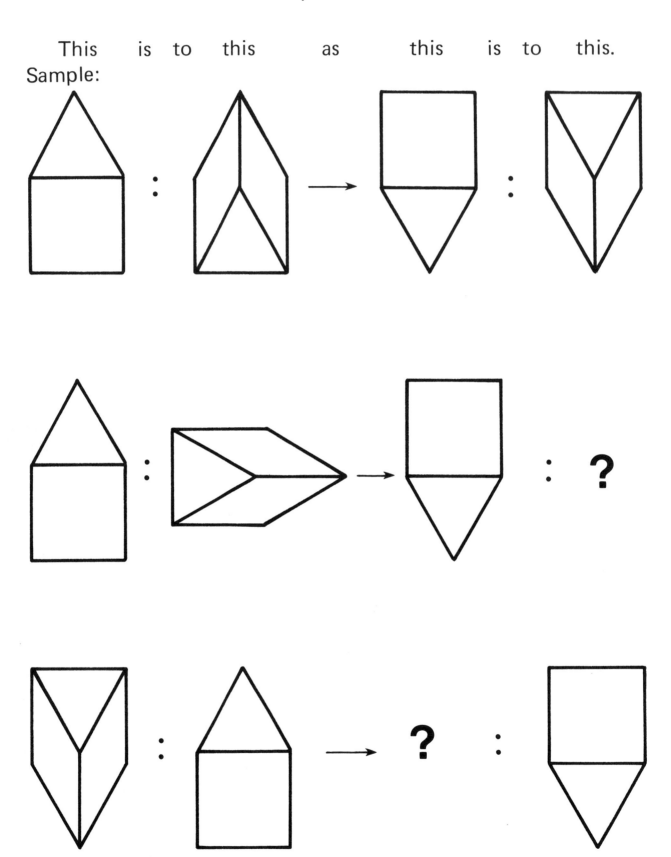

8

Trace your answers.

This is to this as this is to this.

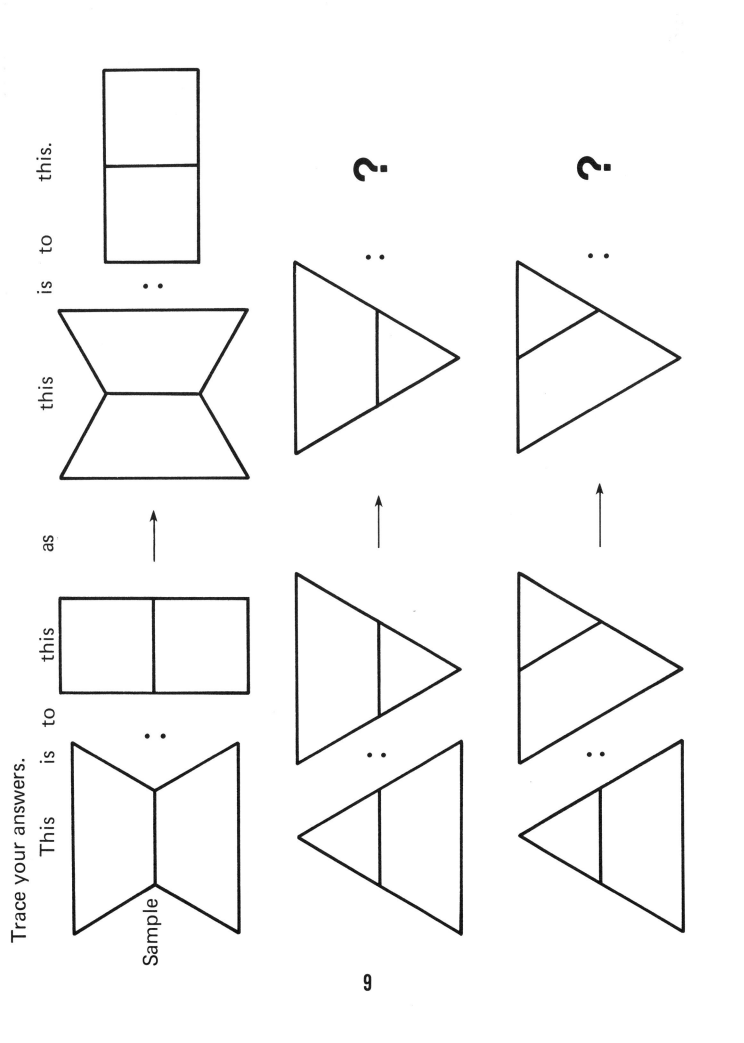

Sample

?

?

9

Trace your answers.

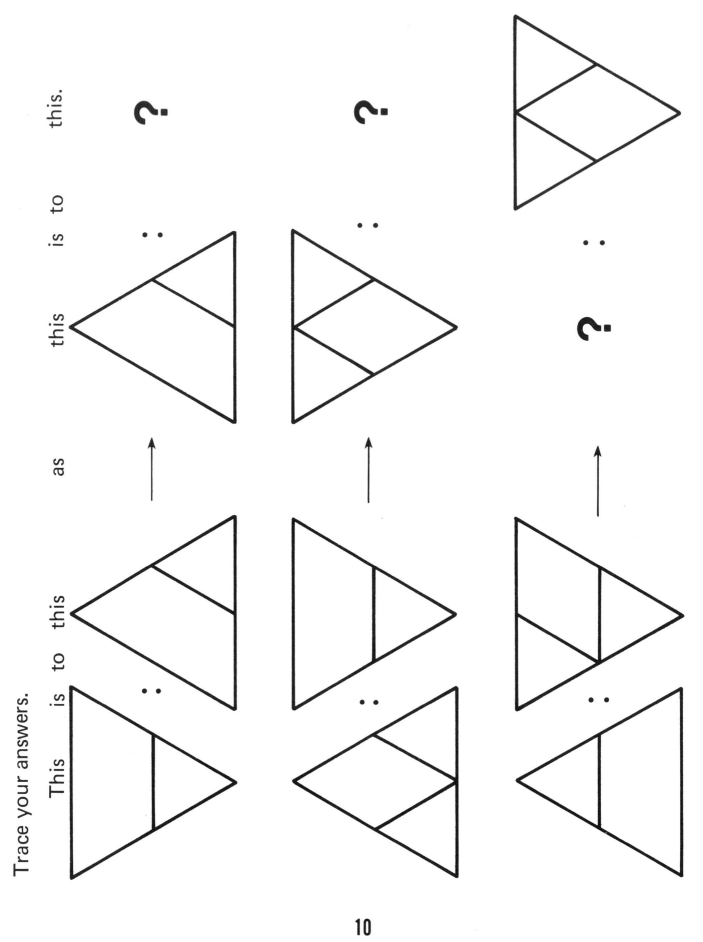

This is to this .. as this is to this ..?.

is to .. ?.

?.

10

Trace your answers.

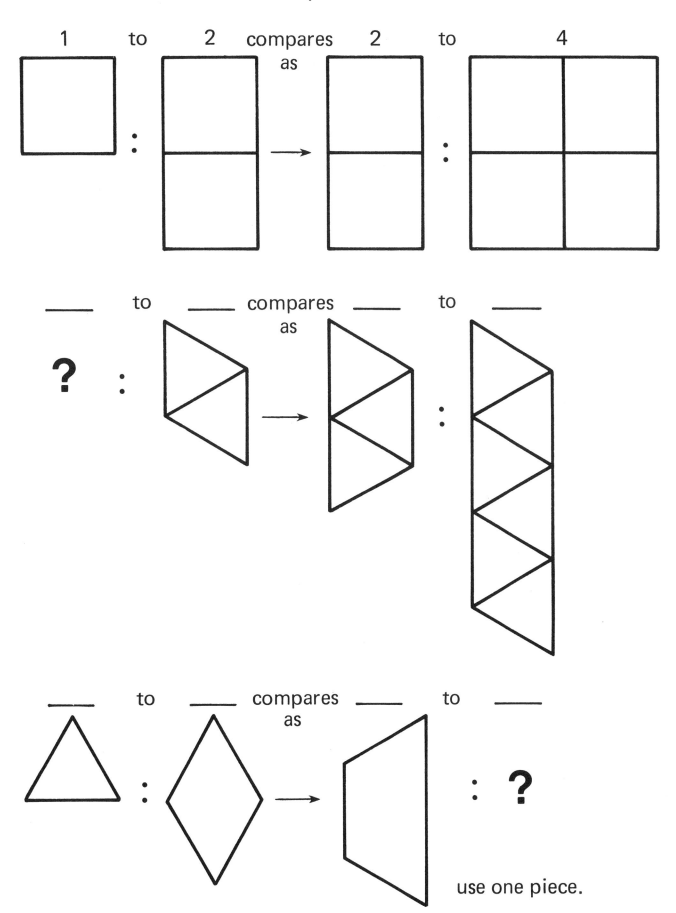

1    to    2    compares    2    to    4
as

___    to    ___    compares    ___    to    ___
as

___    to    ___    compares    ___    to    ___
as

use one piece.

11

# Trace your answers.

_____ to _____ compares _____ to _____
as

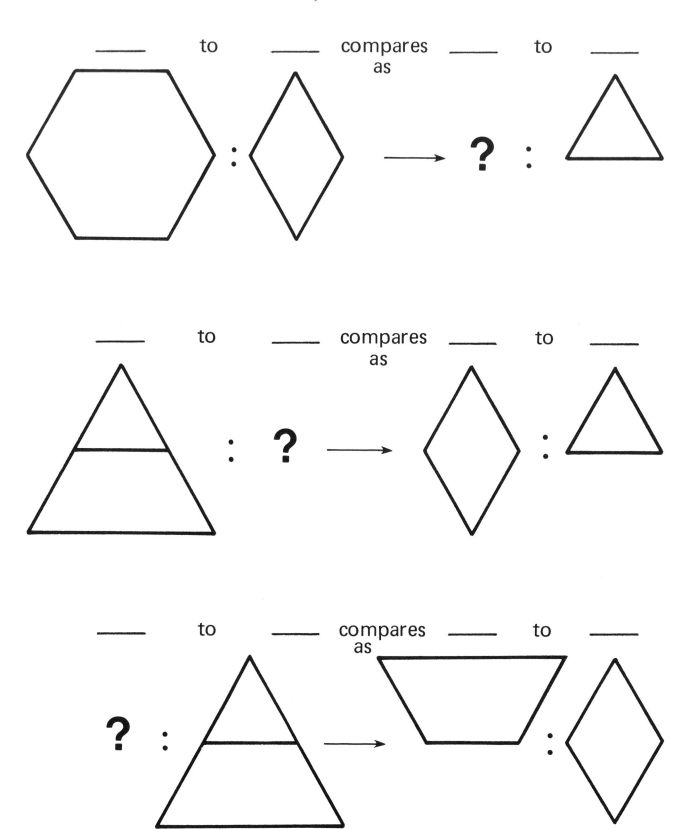

12

_____ to _____ compares as _____ to _____

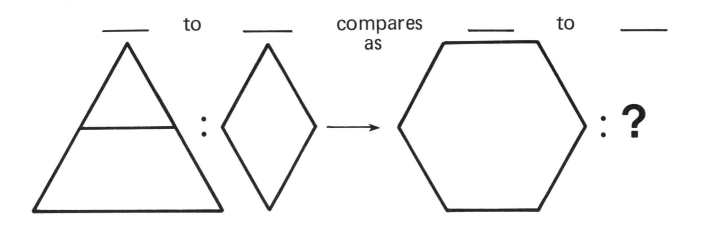

_____ to _____ compares as _____ to _____

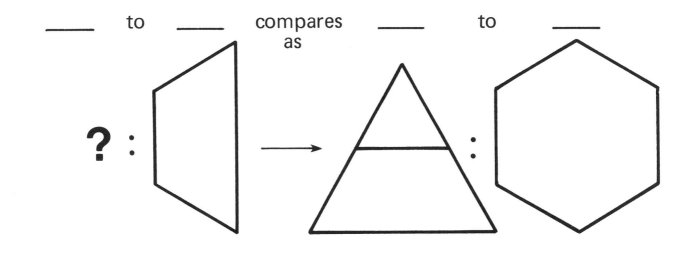

_____ to _____ compares as _____ to _____

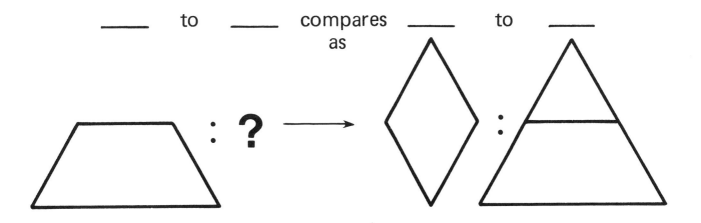

13

What happens when you try to build larger
hexagons using hexagons?

Let's use trapezoids to build hexagons.

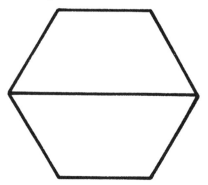

The first hexagon (1) takes _____ blocks.

The second hexagon (2) takes _____ blocks.

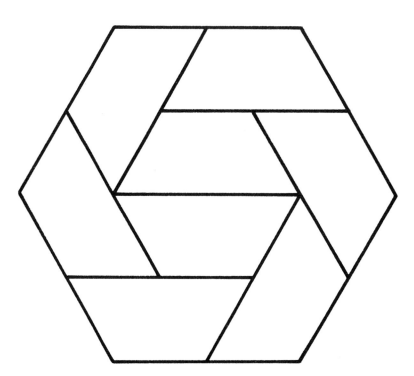

Finish the pattern:

| Number of figure | Blocks used |
|:---:|:---:|
| 3 | _____ |
| 4 | _____ |
| 5 | _____ |

14

When you build hexagons using rhombi
you get a different pattern.

It takes _____ rhombi to make the first hexagon.

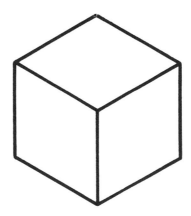

Continue to build hexagons using rhombi.

Complete the table.

| Number of figure | Blocks used |
|:---:|:---:|
| 1 | _____ |
| 2 | _____ |
| 3 | _____ |
| 4 | _____ |
| 5 | _____ |
| 6 | _____ |

Can you tell how many it would take
to make the tenth hexagon?

Can you find a rule for this pattern?

15

When you build hexagons using triangles
you get still a different pattern.

It takes _____ triangles to make the
first hexagon.

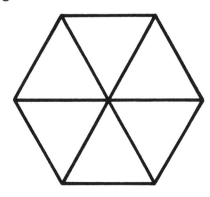

Continue to build hexagons using triangles.

Complete the table.

| Number of figure | Blocks used |
|---|---|
| 1 | 6 |
| 2 | _____ |
| 3 | _____ |
| 4 | _____ |
| 5 | _____ |
| 6 | _____ |

Can you tell how many it takes to make
the tenth hexagon?

Can you find a rule for this pattern?

Now use triangles to build triangles.

 The smallest triangle takes _____ triangle(s).

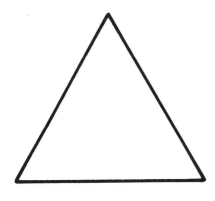 The next size triangle

takes _____ triangles.

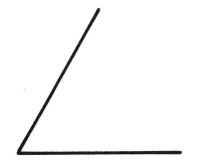 The next size triangle

takes _____ triangles.

Complete the table about triangles built out of triangles.

| Number of figure | Blocks used |
|:---:|:---:|
| 1 | _____ |
| 2 | _____ |
| 3 | _____ |
| 4 | _____ |
| 5 | _____ |
| 6 | _____ |

How many triangles would be in the tenth triangle?

Can you find a rule for the pattern?

18

Building triangles with trapezoids is difficult but it can be done.
Cover this triangle with trapezoids.

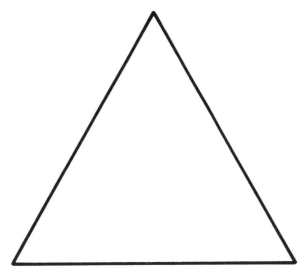

It takes _____ trapezoids to make this triangle.
Can you build the next larger triangle using trapezoids?
It takes _____ trapezoids.

Complete the table about triangles built from trapezoids.

| Number of figure | Blocks used |
| --- | --- |
| 1 | _____ |
| 2 | _____ |
| 3 | _____ |
| 4 | _____ |
| 5 | _____ |
| 6 | _____ |

Have you seen this pattern before?
Can you find the rule for the pattern?

*Perimeter* is the sum of the lengths of the sides of a figure.

The perimeter of [figure: a 1×5 row of squares] is ___12___ units.

The perimeter of [figure: a 2×2 square] is _____ units.

The perimeter of [figure: an irregular shape made of squares] is _____ units.

Draw a shape with a perimeter of 10 units.

Can you draw a different figure with the same perimeter?

For these activities try to find all the
different perimeters from the
smallest number to the largest number.

Rule: All of one side *must* touch all of another side.

o.k.                                    NOT o.k.

Using 12 squares make figures with
perimeters of 14, 16, 18, 20, 22, 24,
and 26 units. Draw the figures below.

14 units                                22 units

16 units                                24 units

18 units                                26 units

20 units

Compare your drawings to those of a friend.
Are they the same?

21

The green triangle has a perimeter of 3 units.

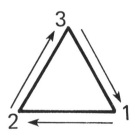

The perimeter of two green triangles together is

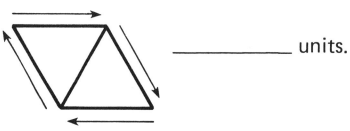 _____ units.

With 12 triangles we can find several figures with perimeters of ten units.

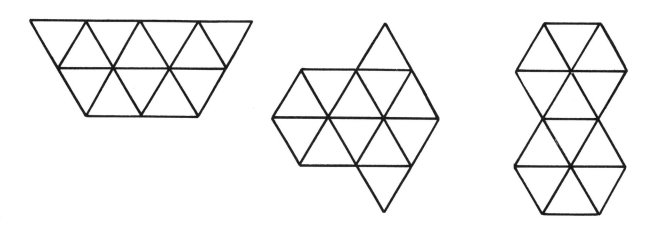

Make other figures with 12 triangles and perimeters of ten units. Record your answers.

Make several figures with 12 triangles and perimeters of 12 units and 14 units.

Using 16 squares make figures with  perimeters of

16 units                              26 units

18 units                              28 units

20 units                              30 units

22 units                              32 units

24 units                              34 units

Compare your drawings with those of a friend.
Are they the same?

Using 16 triangles, the smallest perimeter
you can find is a figure with a perimeter
of_____units. Record other figures you
can make with 16 triangles and perimeters of
of 12 units.

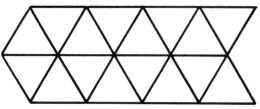

14 units

16 units

18 units

Using ten trapezoids make several
figures with perimeters of

16 units

_____ units

_____ units

_____ units

30 units

*Area* is the space covered by a figure.
It is measured in square units.

The area of □ is____1____square unit.

The area of ⊞ is_____square units.

The area of [grid] is_____square units.

Draw a figure with an area of 16 square units.

Build the next two larger squares that follow the pattern.

Square 1

Perimeter: ____4____ units

Area: ____1____ square unit

Square 2

Perimeter: _____ units

Area: _____ square units

Square 3

Perimeter: _____ units

Area: _____ square units

Square 4

Perimeter: _____ units

Area: _____ square units

27

Complete the table. Check yourself by building the first few figures.

| Square | Units of Perimeter | Square Units of Area | Ratio of Perimeter to Area |
|---|---|---|---|
| 1 | 4 | 1 | 4 to 1 |
| 2 | 8 | 4 | 8 to 4 = 2 to 1 |
| 3 | 12 | 9 | 12 to 9 = 4 to ? |
| 4 | 16 | | |
| 5 | | | |
| 6 | | | |
| 7 | | | |
| 8 | | | |
| | | | |
| | | | |

What patterns do you see?

28

Build the next two oblong rectangles that follow the model.

Rectangle A

Perimeter: _____6_____ units

Area: _____2_____ square units

Rectangle B

Perimeter: _____10_____ units

Area: _____ square units

Rectangle C

Perimeter: _____ units

Area: _____ square units

Rectangle D

Perimeter: _____ units

Area: _____ square units

29

Complete the table. Check yourself by building the first few figures.

| Rec- tangle | Units of Perimeter | Square Units of Area | Ratio of Perimeter to Area |
|---|---|---|---|
| A | 6 | 2 | |
| B | 10 | 6 | |
| C | | | |
| D | | | |
| E | | | |
| F | | | |
| G | | | |
| H | | | |
| | | | |

What patterns can you find?

Build the next two stairs that follow the model.

| Stair 1 | Perimeter | Area |
|---|---|---|

|  | 4 | 1 |

Stair 2

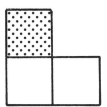

|  | 8 | 1 + 2 = 3 |

Stair 3

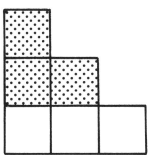

|  | 12 | 1 + 2 + 3 = 6 |

Stair 4                          Record your answers below.

Stair 5

Complete the table. Check yourself by building the first few figures.

| Stair | Units of Perimeter | Square Units of Area | Ratio of Perimeter to Area |
|---|---|---|---|
| 1 | 4 | 1 | 4 to 1 |
| 2 | 8 | 3 | 8 to 3 |
| 3 | | | |
| 4 | | | |
| 5 | | | |
| 6 | | | |
| 7 | | | |
| 8 | | | |
| 9 | | | |

What patterns can you find?

Build the next two *long stairs* that follow the model.

|  | Perimeter | Area |
|---|---|---|
| Long stair 1 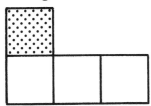 | 4 | 1 |
| Long stair 2 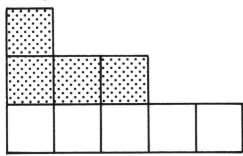 | 10 | 1 + 3 = 4 |
| Long stair 3 | 16 | 1 + 3 + 5 = _____ |
| Long stair 4 | _____ | _____ |
| Long stair 5 | _____ | _____ |

**33** What patterns can you find?

Complete the table. Check yourself by building the first few figures.

| Long stair | Units of Perimeter | Square Units of Area | Ratio of Perimeter to Area |
|---|---|---|---|
| 1 | 4 | 1 | 4 to 1 |
| 2 | | | |
| 3 | | | |
| 4 | | | |
| 5 | | | |
| 6 | | | |
| 7 | | | |
| 8 | | | |
| 9 | | | |

Build the next larger Zig-Zag that follows the model.

Zig-Zag 1

Perimeter: _____ units

Area: _____ square units

Zig-Zag 2

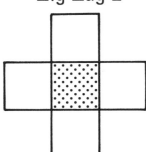

Perimeter: _____ units

Area: _____ square units

Zig-Zag 3

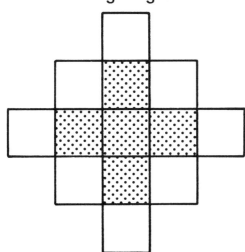

Perimeter: _____ units

Area: _____ square units

Complete the table. Check yourself by building the first few figures.

| Zig-Zag | Units of Perimeter | Square Units of Area | |
|---------|--------------------|----------------------|-----------|
| 1 | 4 | 1 | 4 to 1 |
| 2 | 12 | 5 | 12 to 5 |
| 3 | 20 | 13 | 20 to ? |
| 4 | | | |
| 5 | | | |
| 6 | | | |
| 7 | | | |
| 8 | | | |
| | | | |

What patterns can you find?

Build the next two larger moats that follow the model.

## Moat 1

Outer perimeter: ___12___ units

Inner perimeter: ___4___ units

Total perimeter: ___16___ units

Area: ___8___ square units

## Moat 2

Outer perimeter: _____units

Inner perimeter: _____units

Total perimeter: _____units

Area: _____ square units

## Moat 3

Outer perimeter: _____units

Inner perimeter: _____units

Total perimeter: _____units

Area: _____square units

## Moat 4

Outer perimeter: _____ units

Inner perimeter: _____ units

Total perimeter: _____ units

Area: _____square units

Complete the table. Check yourself by building the first few figures.

| Square moat | Outer Perimeter Units | Inner Perimeter Units | Total Perimeter Units | Area Square Units | Ratio of Total Perimeter to Area |
|---|---|---|---|---|---|
| 1 | 12 | 4 | 16 | 8 | 16 to 8 = 2 to 1 |
| 2 | 16 | 8 | 24 | 12 | 24 to 12 = 2 to 1 |
| 3 | | | | | |
| 4 | | | | | |
| 5 | | | | | |
| 6 | | | | | |
| 7 | | | | | |
| 8 | | | | | |
| 9 | | | | | |

What patterns can you find?

A circle is measured in units called degrees (written °).
A circle always has the same number of degrees: 360.

We can use the circle to help us find the degrees in
the corners, or angles, of the pattern blocks.

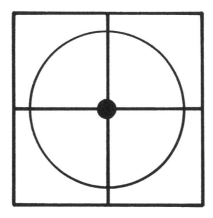

Let's begin with the square. It takes four squares to
cover the circle.

If there are 360° in the circle there are $\frac{1}{4}$ of 360° in
one angle of one square.

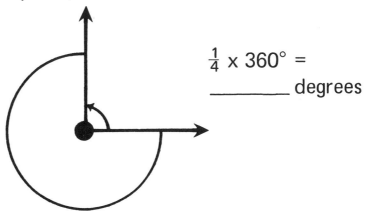

$\frac{1}{4}$ x 360° =

_____ degrees

How many degrees in each of the other angles of the
square?

Since we know there are 360° in a circle we can find the degrees in the angles of each of the pattern block pieces.

It takes _____ green triangles to cover the circle, so each small angle measures _____ of 360° or _____degrees.

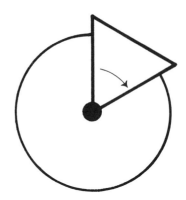

If we use the small corner, it takes _____ blue rhombi to cover the circle, so each small angle measures _____ of 360° or _____ degrees.

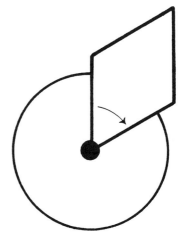

If we use the small corner, it takes_____ red trapezoids to cover the circle, so each small angle measures_____ of _____or _____ degrees.

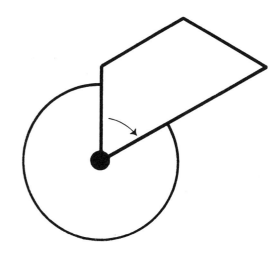

Find the measures of
the large angle of
the blue diamond.

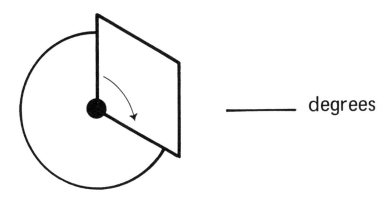 _____ degrees

the large angle of
the red trapezoid.

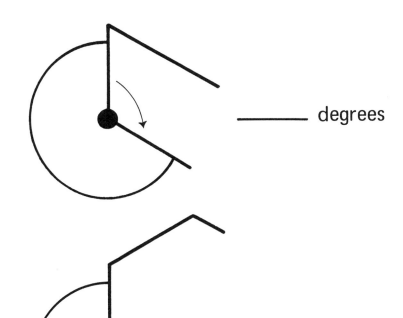 _____ degrees

the angle of the
yellow hexagon.

_____ degrees

the small angle of
the tan rhombus.

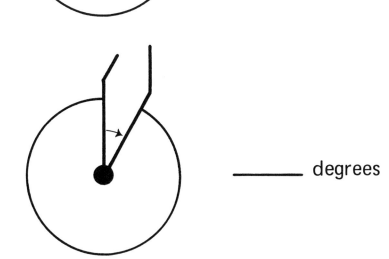 _____ degrees

Find the measure of
the square and the
blue rhombus
_____ °

the hexagon and
a blue rhombus
_____ °

the small angle and the
large angle of the
trapezoid
_____ °

the hexagon and
the large angle of a
tan rhombus
_____ °

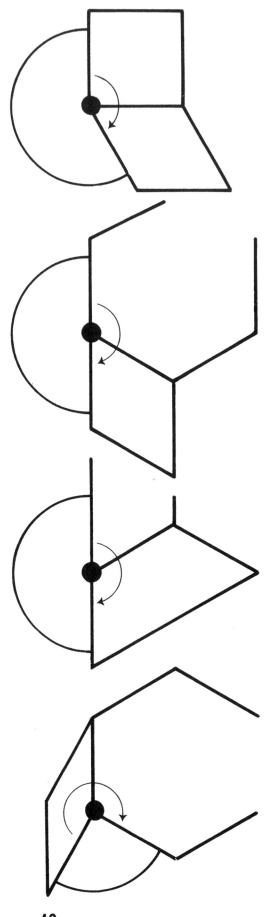

42

A shape is symmetric if one part is a mirror image of the other part. The line of symmetry is where you put the mirror so the reflection is the same as what is behind the mirror. For example,

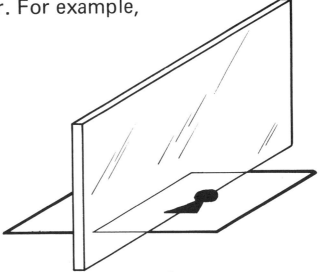

The reflection in the mirror here completes the keyhole. The line of symmetry in this picture is where the mirror is.

Use a mirror to find if these shapes are symmetric. Draw a line of symmetry if it exists. For example,

Shapes often have more than one line of symmetry.
Draw a different line of symmetry on each square.

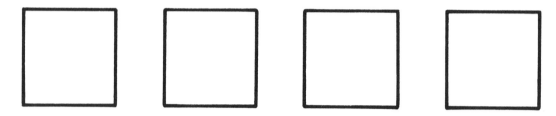

Draw all of the lines of symmetry you can find on
these shapes.

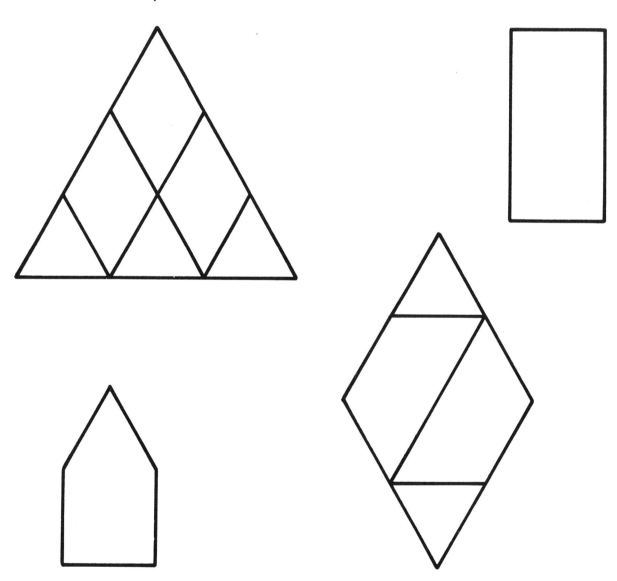

Draw some symmetric shapes. Show the lines of symmetry.
Draw other shapes that are not symmetric.

Symmetry: Point-to-point

How many lines of symmetry can you find if you put
two green triangles together point-to-point like this?

Draw the lines of symmetry.

 _____ line(s) of symmetry

How many lines of symmetry can you find if
you put two green triangles together point-to-
point like this?

Draw the lines of symmetry.

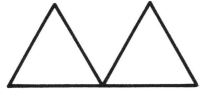 _____ line(s) of symmetry

How many other ways can you find to put two
green triangles together point-to-point so
that there is at least one line of symmetry?

45

How many lines of symmetry can you find if you put two orange squares together point-to-point like this?

Draw the lines of symmetry.

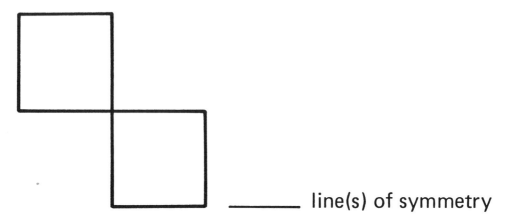

_____ line(s) of symmetry

Find other ways to put two orange squares together point-to-point so that there is at least one
line of symmetry. Show your answers here.

If you put two blue rhombi together point-to-point like this

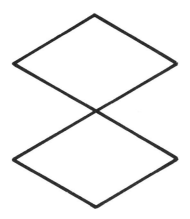

you can find two lines of symmetry. How many other ways can you find to put two blue rhombi together point-to-point so that there are at least two lines of symmetry?

If you put two blue rhombi together point-to-point like this

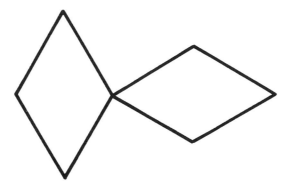

you can find only one line of symmetry. How many other ways can you find to put two blue rhombi together point-to-point so that there is one line of symmetry?

Does the tan rhombus have the same patterns?

How many ways can you put two yellow
hexagons together point-to-point in order
to find two lines of symmetry?
one line  of symmetry?
no  lines of symmetry?

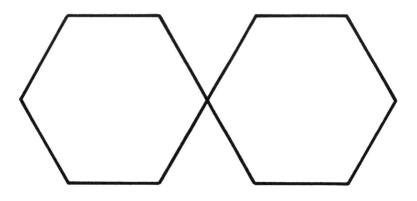

Record your answers here.

How many lines of symmetry can you find in each of these?
Draw them.

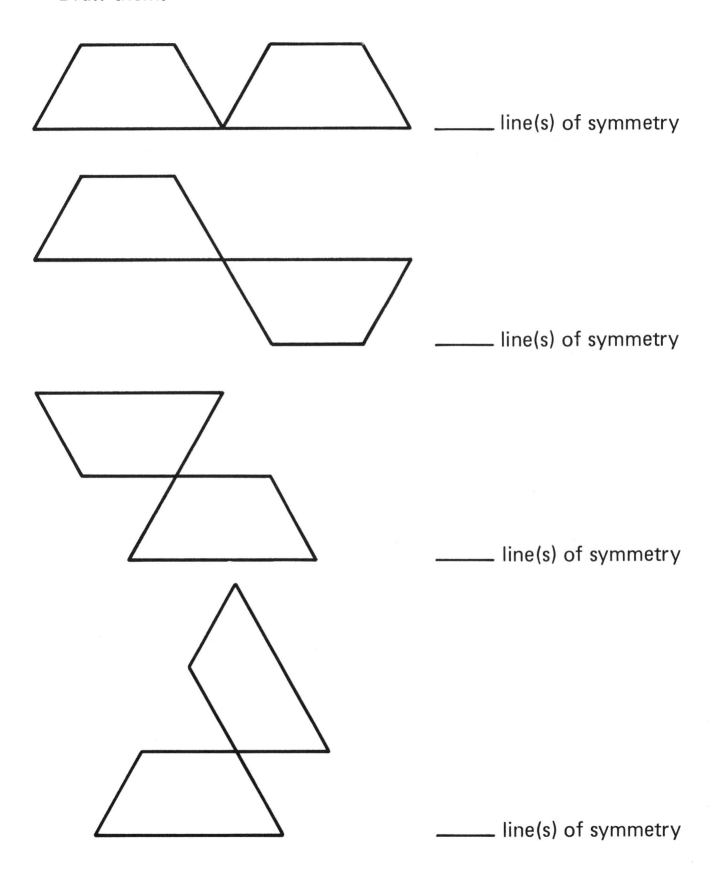

_____ line(s) of symmetry

_____ line(s) of symmetry

_____ line(s) of symmetry

_____ line(s) of symmetry

49

Complete the top half so that the dotted line is a line of symmetry. Find other lines of symmetry in the completed design.

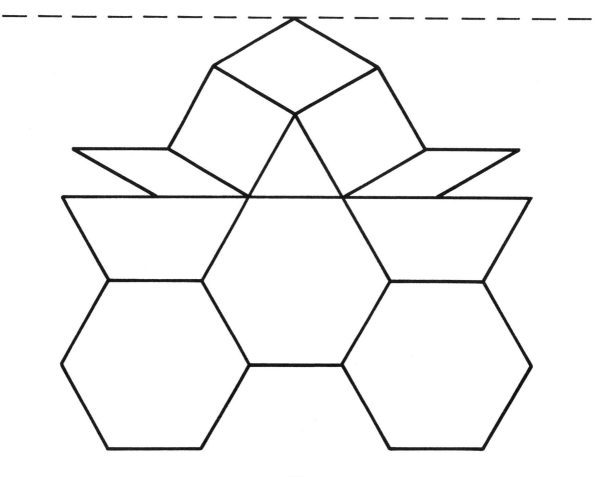

50

Complete the design by making the same pattern on all four sides of the orange square. (Each side is started for you.) How many lines of symmetry can you find?

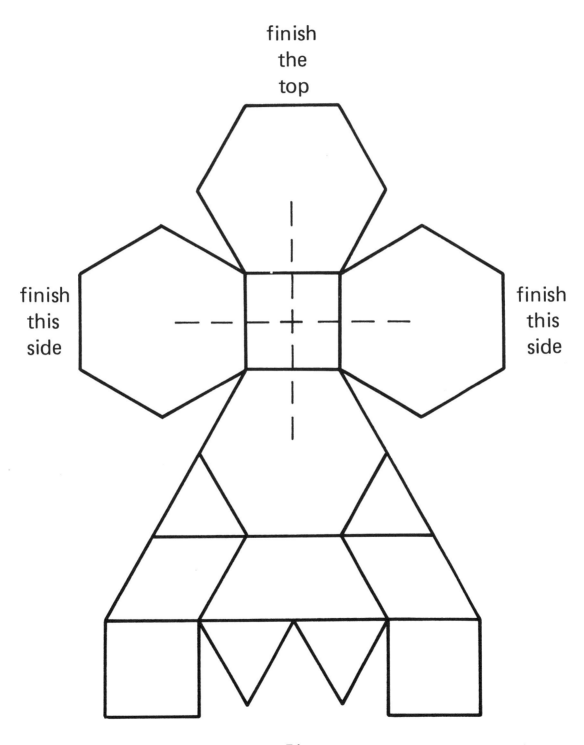

finish
the
top

finish
this
side

finish
this
side

Complete the design so that it has four lines of symmetry.
(Hint: there will be four orange squares in the center.)

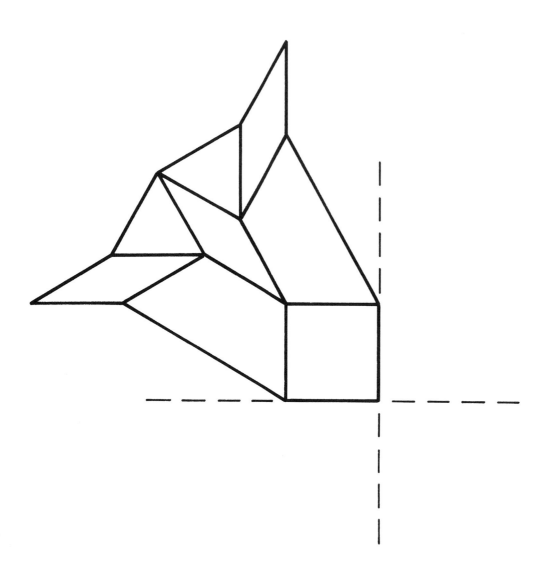

Complete the design by repeating the pattern on all four sides of the tan rhombus. How many lines of symmetry can you find?

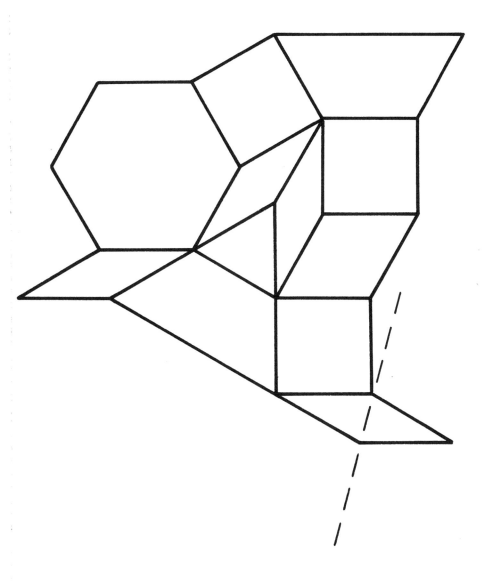

53

Complete the design by building on all three sides of
the triangle. (There will be an orange square on all
sides of the triangle.) How many lines of symmetry
can you find?

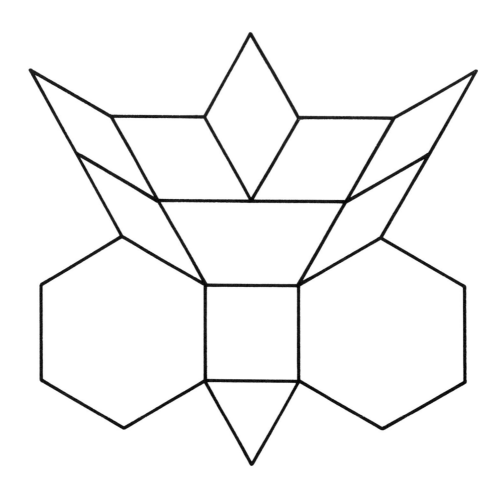

# POLYGONS

A *polygon* is a simple closed figure whose sides are straight line segments.

Shade in the polygons.

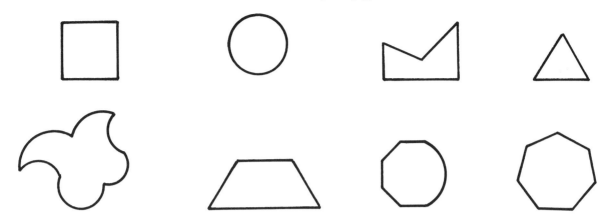

Draw some polygons and ask a friend to check them.

55

# CONGRUENT POLYGONS

Some polygons have special names depending upon how many sides they have.

All polygons with three sides are called *triangles*.

Find three pattern block pieces that are triangles. Outline them here.

How are they alike? How are they different?

Figures which are exactly the same in size and shape are called *congruent* figures. Are these triangles congruent?

All polygons with four sides are called *quadrilaterals*.

Find four different pattern block pieces that are quadrilaterals. Draw around them here.

Are any of these quadrilaterals congruent?

Are the sides of any of these figures congruent?

Are the corners, or angles, of any of these figures congruent?

Draw around any congruent angles you find among these four quadrilaterals.

All polygons with six sides are called *hexagons*.

Find three pattern block pieces that are hexagons.
Draw around them here.

Are any of these figures congruent?

Are the angles of any of the other pattern block
pieces congruent to the angle of the hexagon?

Can you find any other angles of pattern block
pieces which are congruent?

Using pattern block pieces, we can make similar figures by letting the figure grow.

*Similar* here means the same shape but a different size.

Here is a triangle which is 2 units on each side.

Make a similar triangle which is 3 units on each side.

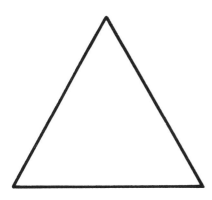

Here is a square which is 1 unit on each side.

Make a similar square which is 3 units on each side.

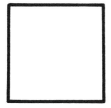

Here is a rhombus
which is 2 units on
each side.

Make a similar rhombus
which is 3 units on
each side.

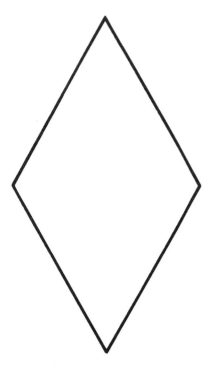

Here is a trapezoid
which is 1 unit on the
top and sides and 2
units on the bottom.

Make a similar trapezoid
which is 2 units on the
top and sides and 4
units on the bottom.

Can you build other similar figures using the pattern block pieces?

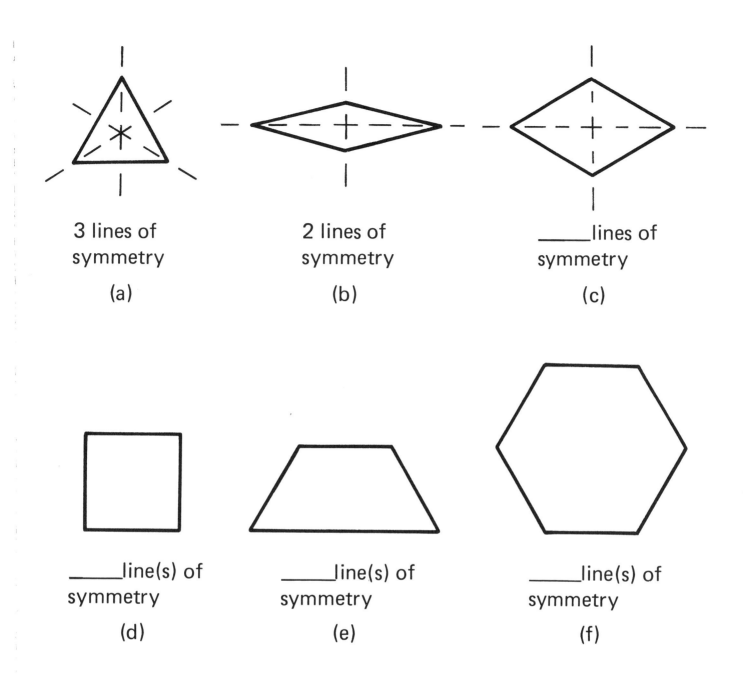

3 lines of
symmetry

(a)

2 lines of
symmetry

(b)

_____lines of
symmetry

(c)

_____line(s) of
symmetry

(d)

_____line(s) of
symmetry

(e)

_____line(s) of
symmetry

(f)

A regular polygon has as many lines of symmetry
as it has sides.  Which of the above are regular
polygons?   _____   _____   _____

Fill this using one kind of pattern block
which is shaped like a regular polygon.

Fill this using one kind of pattern block
which is shaped like a regular polygon.

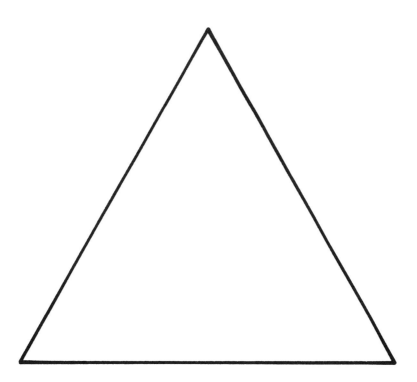

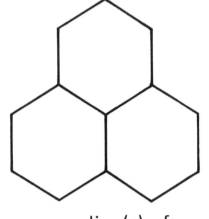

_____ line(s) of
symmetry

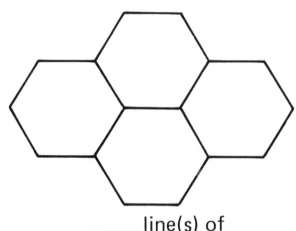

_____ line(s) of
symmetry

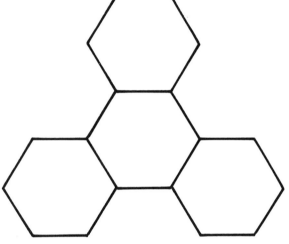

_____ line(s) of
symmetry

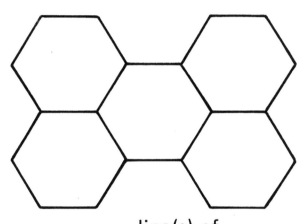

_____ line(s) of
symmetry

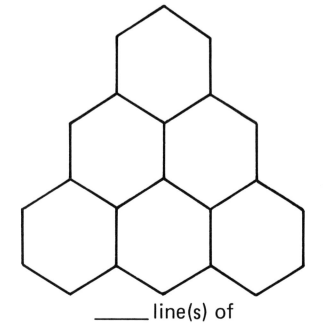

_____ line(s) of
symmetry

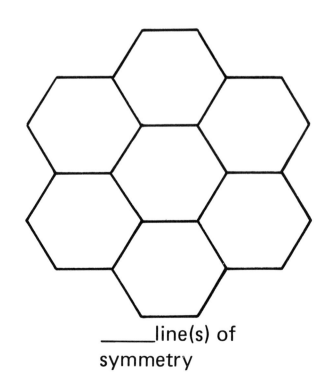

_____ line(s) of
symmetry

Fill this using two kinds of pattern blocks which are shaped like regular polygons.

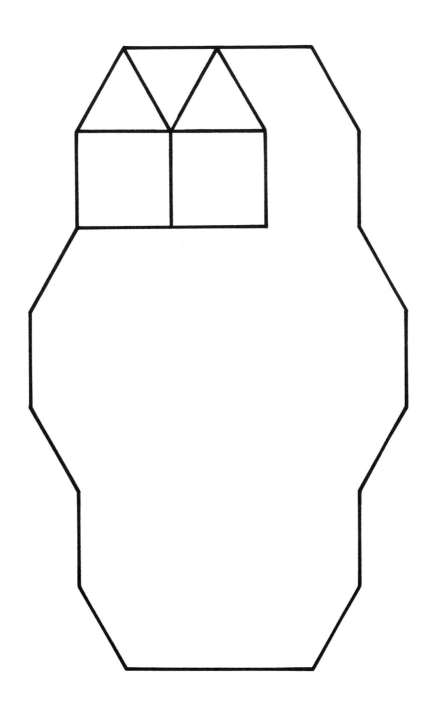

Fill this with these two kinds of pattern blocks.
It will take only 19 blocks to complete the design.

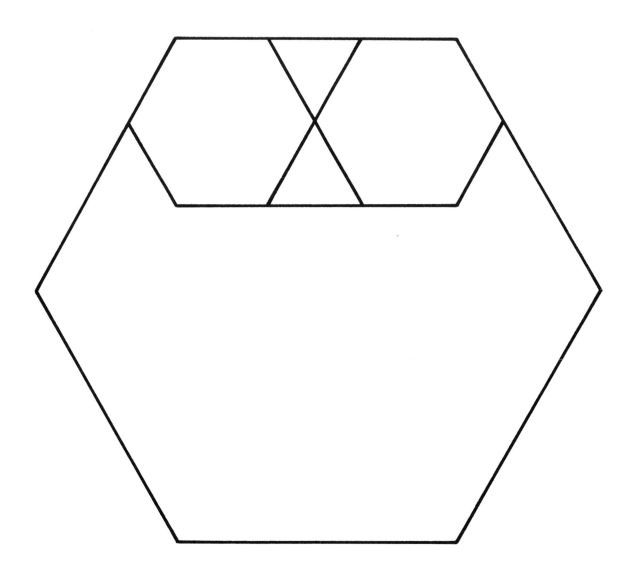

Can you extend this pattern?

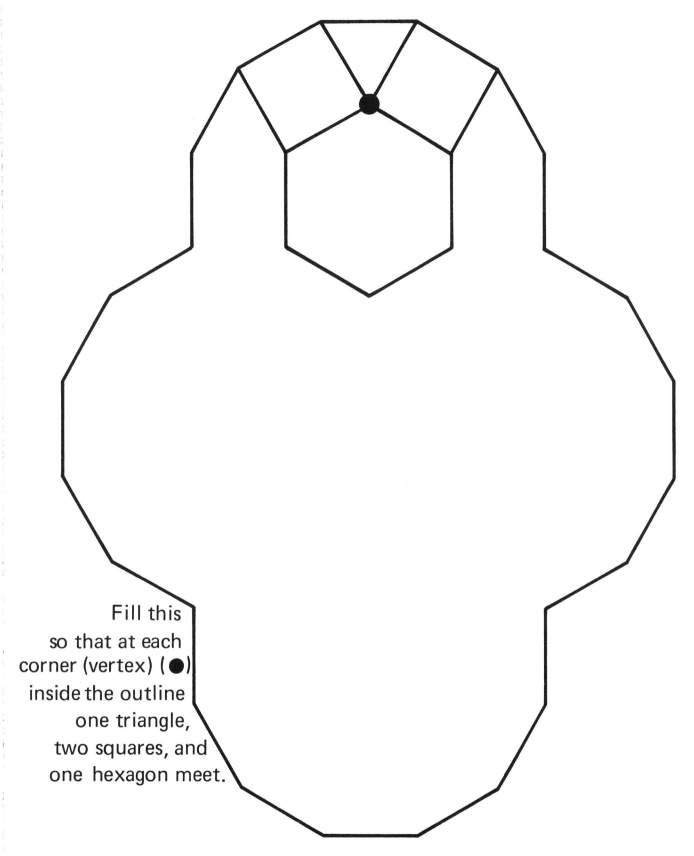

Fill this
so that at each
corner (vertex) (●)
inside the outline
one triangle,
two squares, and
one hexagon meet.

Can you extend the pattern?

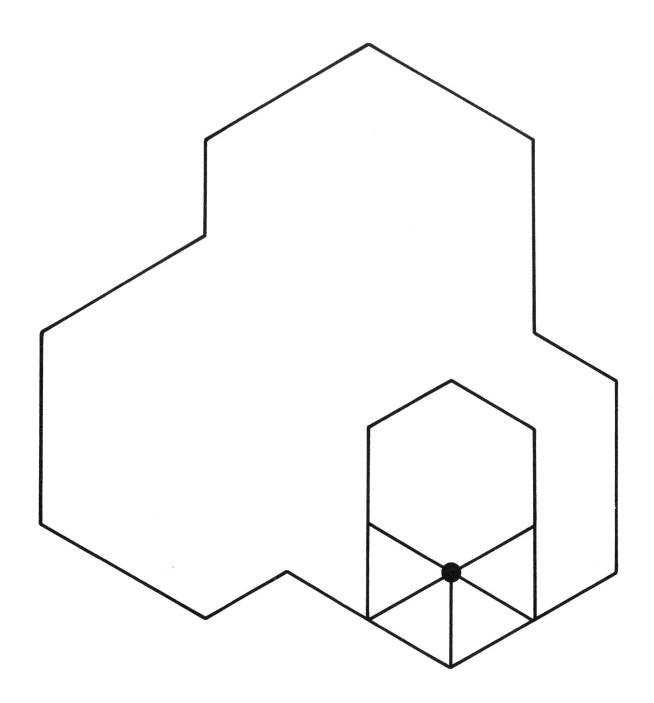

Fill this in so that each corner (vertex) inside the outline has four triangles and one hexagon meeting at each vertex (●).

Can you extend the pattern?

Fill this in using і                    blocks which
are shaped like re

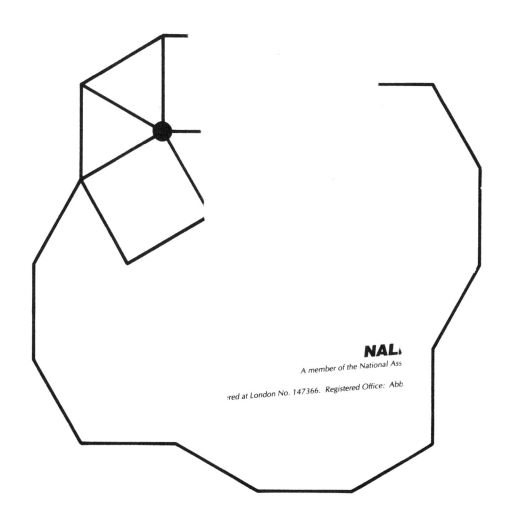

Can you extend the pattern?

# Naming Regular Tessellations

Number names can be helpful to describe what appears at a vertex of a regular tessellation. A block is named for the number of sides it has.

For example,

| Figure | Long name for shapes at vertex | Short name |
|---|---|---|

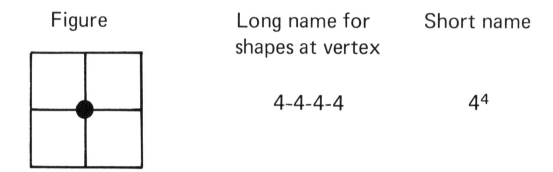

4-4-4-4          $4^4$

Describe the shapes that meet at the vertices of these tessellations.

Long Name          Short Name

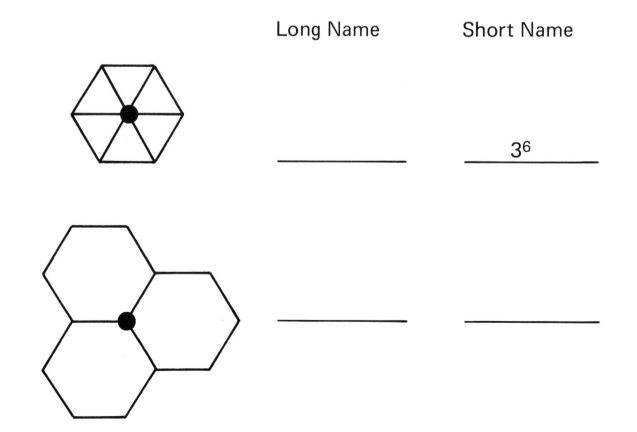

$3^6$

# Naming Semi-Regular Tessellations

A tessellation with more than one kind of regular polygon may have several names.

Example:

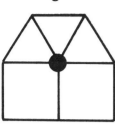

| Figure | Long Names | Short Names | |
|---|---|---|---|
| | a. 4-4-3-3-3 | $4^2$-$3^3$ | Notice how the |
| | b. 4-3-3-3-4 | $4$-$3^3$-$4$ | names describe |
| | c. 3-3-3-4-4 | $3^3$-$4^2$ | the faces in order |
| | d. 3-3-4-4-3 | $3^2$-$4^2$-$3$ | going around the |
| | e. 3-4-4-3-3 | $3$-$4^2$-$3^2$ | vertex. |

Mathematicians agree to use the name that gives the ordered sequence beginning with the lowest number.

Which name would be the best one to use for the semi-regular tessellation above?

Now try these:

A

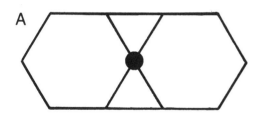

Long Name: _____

Short Name: _____

C

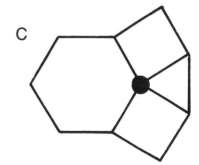

Long Name: _____

Short Name: _____

B

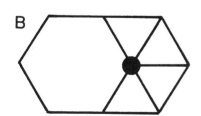

Long Name: _____

Short Name: _____

D

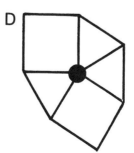

Long Name:

_____

Short Name:

_____

71

# ECONOMY WITH PATTERN BLOCKS

To limit the number of solutions for some pattern block puzzles the Economy Rule may be used. The rule states that any time two or more pattern block pieces that are touching may be replaced by one piece, this must be done.

Examples:

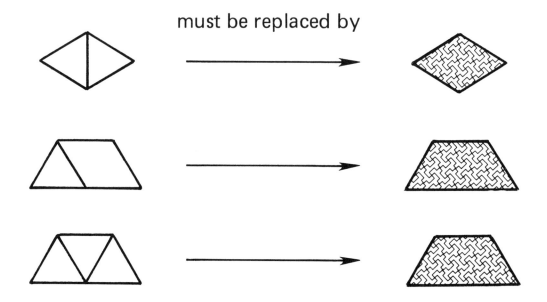

Find at least seven different combinations that must be replaced by one piece.

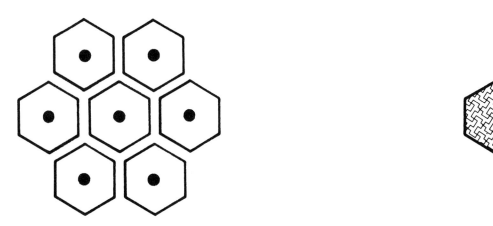

Solutions to these puzzles follow the "Economy Rule."

Complete the table and
fill in the dodecagons using:

|  | Y | R | B | G | O | T | Total |
|---|---|---|---|---|---|---|---|
| a. | //// | //// | //// | 12 | //// | 12 | |
| b. | 1 | //// | //// | 6 | 6 | //// | |

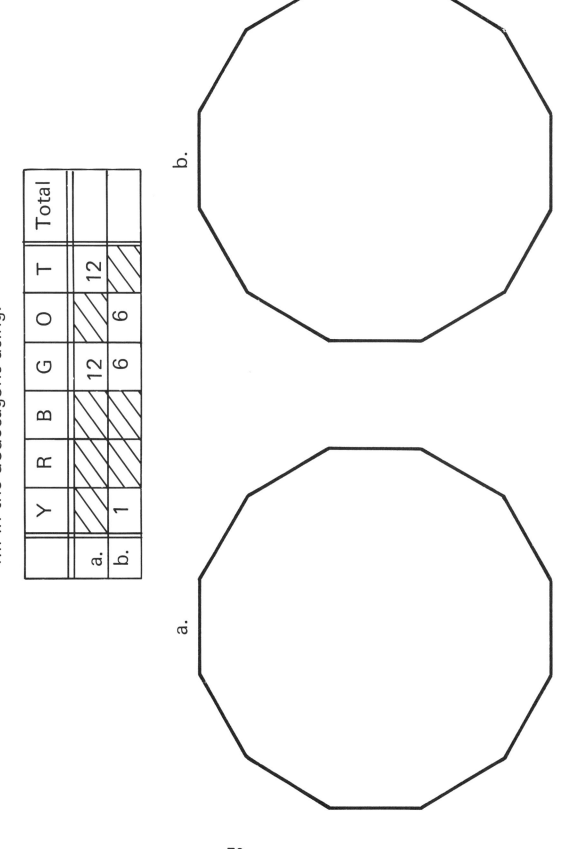

b.

a.

Complete the table and fill in the dodecagons using:

| | Y | R | B | G | O | T | Total |
|---|---|---|---|---|---|---|---|
| a. | /// | | /// | /// | 4 | 4 | 12 |
| b. | /// | 4 | /// | /// | 3 | | 13 |

a.

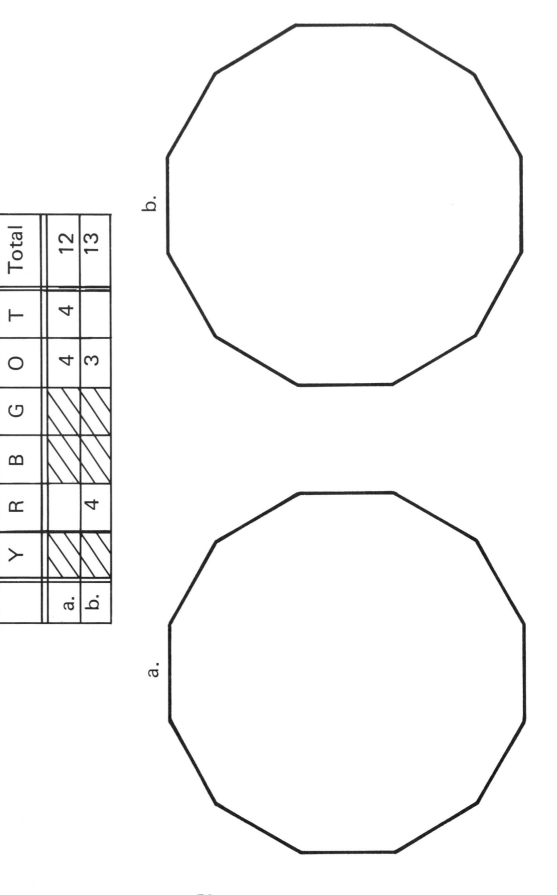

b.

74

Fill in the dodecagons using the shapes
that are not shaded. Then complete the table.

| | Y | R | B | G | O | T | Total |
|---|---|---|---|---|---|---|---|
| a. | | /// | /// | | /// | 12 | 20 |
| b. | | /// | /// | 12 | | | 20 |

a.

b.

Fill in the dodecagons using the shapes that are not shaded. Then complete the table.

| | Y | R | B | G | O | T | Total |
|---|---|---|---|---|---|---|---|
| a. | | //// | | | //// | 12 | 21 |
| b. | | //// | //// | 12 | | | 21 |

a.

b.

Fill in the dodecagons using the shapes that are not shaded. Then complete the table.

| | Y | R | B | G | O | T | Total |
|---|---|---|---|---|---|---|---|
| a. | | ╱╱ | ╱╱ | ╱╱ | | | 11 |
| b. | | ╱╱ | ╱╱ | | | | 18 |

a.

b.

Fill in the dodecagons using the shapes that are not shaded. Then complete the table.

| | Y | R | B | G | O | T | Total |
|---|---|---|---|---|---|---|---|
| a. | ▨ | | | | | | 18 |
| b. | | | | | | | 12 |

a.

b.

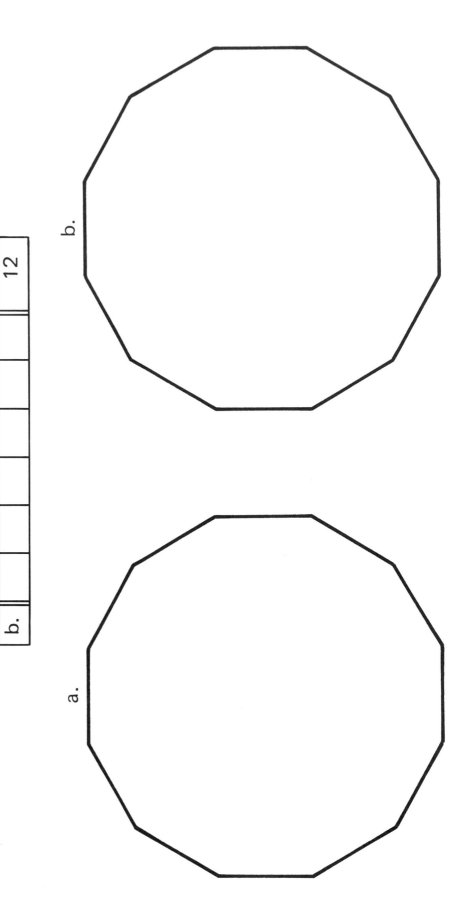

Fill in the dodecagons using the shapes
that are not shaded. Then complete the table.

| | Y | R | B | G | O | T | Total |
|---|---|---|---|---|---|---|---|
| a. | 1 | //// | 6 | //// | | 12 | |
| b. | 1 | 2 | //// | //// | 4 | 4 | |

a.

b.

Fill in the dodecagons using the shapes that are not shaded. Then complete the table.

|  | Y | R | B | G | O | T | Total |
|---|---|---|---|---|---|---|---|
| a. | ▨ | 4 | ▨ | ▨ |  | 8 | 14 |
| b. | ▨ | ▨ | ▨ | ▨ | 3 | 6 | 15 |

a.

b.

Fill in the dodecagons using the shapes that are not shaded. Then complete the table.

| | Y | R | B | G | O | T | Total |
|---|---|---|---|---|---|---|---|
| a. | ▧ | 1 | | | | 4 | 14 |
| b. | ▧ | | | 1 | | 6 | 14 |

b.

a.

81

Fill in the dodecagons using the shapes that are not shaded. Then complete the table.

| | Y | R | B | G | O | T | Total |
|---|---|---|---|---|---|---|---|
| a. | //// | | 1 | | | 8 | 17 |
| b. | //// | | | | 1 | 10 | 17 |

a.

b.

# Extension Appendix A

Find as many different rectangles with 16 units of perimeter as you can. Record your answers in a table like this:

| Picture | Dimensions | Perimeter | Area (square units) |
|---|---|---|---|
| ![1 x 7 rectangle] | 1 x 7 | 16 | 7 |
| ![2 x 6 rectangle] | 2 x 6 | 16 | 12 |
| 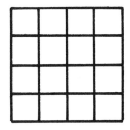 | | | |
| ![4 x 4 square] | | | |

Now try the same thing for 20 units of perimeter.

Can you discover the rule for finding perimeter if you know the length and width of a rectangle?

Can you discover the rule for area?

# Extension Appendix B

| Figure | Area | Perimeter | No. of squares of any size | Inner edges (I) | P+I | (P+I)÷4 |
|---|---|---|---|---|---|---|
| □ | 1 | 4 | 1 | 0 | 4 | 1 |
| | 4 | 8 | 5 | 4 | 12 | 3 |
| | | | | | | |
| | | | | | | |

| Sponges | Area (A) | Perimeter (P) | Inner Edge (I) | P+I | (P+I)÷4 |
|---|---|---|---|---|---|
| | 1 | 4 | 0 | 4 | 1 |
| | 5 | 20 | 0 | 20 | 5 |
| | | | 16 | | |
| ? | | | | | |

Experiment:

1.  Tape together two mirrors end-to-end like this:

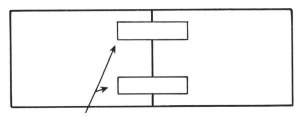

    (tape on back of mirrors)

2.  Use one square block and the two taped mirrors:

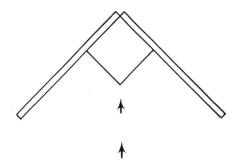

3.  How many squares do you see? Why?

4.  Try this with the hexagon and triangle.
    What do you see? Why?

5.  Now try this with the blue rhombus, the tan rhombus
    and the trapezoid. Try this with both kinds of angles on
    each figure.

# Extension Appendix D

## 1     Symmetry: Two different pieces side-by-side

Put two different pattern block pieces together side-by-side so that . . .

1. all of one side touches all of another side
2. there is at least one line of symmetry
3. all of both pieces show when you find the line of symmetry.

This figure follows the rules . . .

at least one line of symmetry and both pieces show.

This figure does not follow the rules . . .

at least one line of symmetry but both pieces do not show.

Can you find the five other figures which follow the rules and show them here?

## 2     Symmetry: Side centered on side

Put two different pattern block pieces together so that . . .

1. all of one side is centered against another side
2. there is at least one line of symmetry
3. all of both pieces show.

This figure follows the rules . . .

at least one line of symmetry and all of both pieces show.

Can you find the three other figures and show them here?

## 3

Find at least six ways to put two different pieces together point-to-point so that you find at least one line of symmetry.

Draw your figures and show the line(s) of symmetry.

Example:

## 4

We have used three ways of putting pieces together to find lines of symmetry:

side-to-side     

side to half side     

point-to-point     

Two pieces may also be put together point-to-side.

Find at least six more ways of putting two pieces together point-to-side, so that you can find a line of symmetry.

**87**

| Picture | Name | Number of sides or angles $n$ | Fewest number of triangles $n-2$ | Total interior degrees $180°(n-2)$ | Measure of interior angle $\dfrac{180°(n-2)}{n}$ | Measure of central angle $\dfrac{360°}{n}$ |
|---|---|---|---|---|---|---|
| | triangle | 3 | 1 | 180° | 60° | 120° |
| | square | 4 | 2 | 360° | 90° | 90° |
| | pentagon | 5 | | | | |
| | hexagon | 6 | | | | |
| | heptagon | 7 | | | | |
| | octagon | | | | | |

sum is always 180°

Given edge length and measure of interior angle draw a regular polygon.

Example: Draw a square with edge length of 4 cm. (We know how to find interior angle measure from chart on previous page.)

1.   Draw a line 4 cm long:

2.   Place protractor at one end and mark a 90° angle.

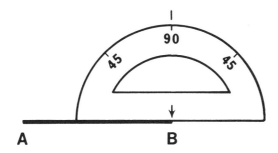

A                                  B

3.   Draw 90° angle so that each side of angle is 4 cm long.

4.   Now mark 90° angle at C and draw $\overline{CD}$ to be 4 cm long.

A                                  B

5.   Continue until figure closes.

Construct a regular polygon within a circle using a protractor, compass and known central angle (from chart on page 88).

Example: triangle

1. Draw circle
2. Mark in a radius ($\overline{AB}$)
3. Measure 120° angle at B
4. Draw in $\overline{BC}$

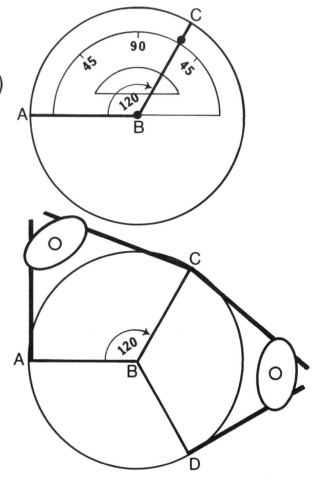

5. Set compass points for distance of arc AC and mark arc CD ≅ arc AC

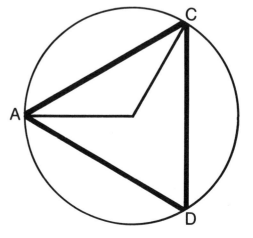

6. Connect points ACD to form triangle

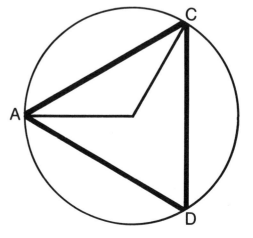

# Solutions

**Page 1.**
2
3
6
3
2

**Page 2.** $\frac{1}{2}$    $\frac{1}{3}$
$\frac{1}{6}$    $\frac{1}{6} + \frac{1}{3} = \frac{1}{2}$
$\frac{1}{2} + \frac{1}{3} = \frac{5}{6}$
$\frac{1}{2} + \frac{1}{2} = 1$

**Page 3.**

**Page 4.**

**Page 5.**

**Page 6.**

**Page 7.**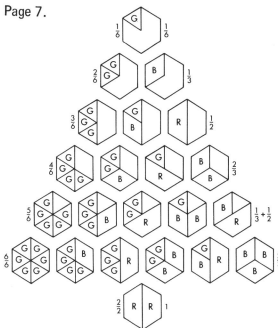

**Page 8.**

**Page 9.**

**Page 10.**

**Page 11.** 1 to 2 compares as 3 to 6

1 to 2 compares as 3 to 6

91

Page 12. 6 to 2 compares as 3 to 1

4 to 2 compares as 2 to 1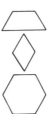

6 to 4 compares as 3 to 2

Page 13. 4 to 2 compares as 6 to 3

2 to 3 compares as 4 to 6

3 to 6 compares as 2 to 4

Page 14. It can't be done.
2 blocks
8 blocks

| x No. of fig. | y Blocks used |
|---|---|
| 3 | 18 |
| 4 | 32 |
| 5 | 50 |

Rule: $y = 2x^2$

Page 15. 3

| x No. of fig. | y Blocks used |
|---|---|
| 1 | 3 |
| 2 | 12 |
| 3 | 27 |
| 4 | 48 |
| 5 | 75 |
| 6 | 108 |

Rule: $y = 3x^2$

Page 16. 6

| x No. of fig. | y Blocks used |
|---|---|
| 1 | 6 |
| 2 | 24 |
| 3 | 54 |
| 4 | 96 |
| 5 | 150 |
| 6 | 216 |

Rule: $y = 6x^2$

Page 17. 1    4    9

Page 18.

| x No. of fig. | y Blocks used |
|---|---|
| 1 | 1 |
| 2 | 4 |
| 3 | 9 |
| 4 | 16 |
| 5 | 25 |
| 10 | 100 |

Rule: $y = x^2$

Page 19. 3
12

| x No. of fig. | y Blocks used |
|---|---|
| 1 | 3 |
| 2 | 12 |
| 3 | 27 |
| 4 | 48 |
| 5 | 75 |

Rule: $y = 3x^2$

Page 20. 8
22

Page 22. 4

Page 24. 12

Page 26. 4
15

Page 27  Square 1    perimeter: 4
area: 1 square unit
Square 2    perimeter: 8
area: 4 square units
Square 3    perimeter: 12
area: 9
Square 4    perimeter: 16
area: 16

92

Page 28.

| square | perimeter | area | Ratio of P to A |
|--------|-----------|------|------------------|
| 1 | 4 | 1 | 4 to 1 |
| 2 | 8 | 4 | 8 to 4 = 4 to 2 |
| 3 | 12 | 9 | 12 to 9 = 4 to 3 |
| 4 | 16 | 16 | 16 to 16 = 4 to 4 |
| 5 | 20 | 25 | 20 to 25 = 4 to 5 |
| 6 | 24 | 36 | 24 to 36 = 4 to 6 |
| 7 | 28 | 49 | 28 to 49 = 4 to 7 |
| 8 | 32 | 64 | 32 to 64 = 4 to 8 |

Page 29.  Rectangle A    perimeter: 6
                        area: 2
          Rectangle B    perimeter: 10
                        area: 6
          Rectangle C    perimeter: 14
                        area: 12
          Rectangle C    perimeter: 18
                        area: 20

Page 30.

| Rectangle | Units of perimeter (P) | Square units of area (A) | Ratio of P to A |
|-----------|------------------------|--------------------------|------------------|
| A | 6 | 2 | 6 to 2 = 3 to 1 |
| B | 10 | 6 | 10 to 6 = 5 to 3 |
| C | 14 | 12 | 14 to 12 = 7 to 6 |
| D | 18 | 20 | 18 to 20 = 9 to 10 |
| E | 22 | 30 | 22 to 30 = 11 to 15 |
| F | 26 | 42 | 26 to 42 = 13 to 21 |
| G | 30 | 56 | 30 to 56 = 15 to 28 |
| H | 34 | 72 | 34 to 72 = 17 to 36 |

Page 31.  16   1 + 2 + 3 + 4 = 10
          20   1 + 2 + 3 + 4 + 5 = 15

Page 32.

| Stair | Units of perimeter (P) | Square Units of area (A) | Ratio of P to A |
|-------|------------------------|--------------------------|------------------|
| 1 | 4 | 1 | 4 to 1 |
| 2 | 8 | 3 | 8 to 3 |
| 3 | 12 | 6 | 12 to 6 = 2 to 1 |
| 4 | 16 | 10 | 16 to 10 = 8 to 5 |
| 5 | 20 | 15 | 20 to 15 = 5 to 3 |
| 6 | 24 | 21 | 24 to 21 = 8 to 7 |
| 7 | 28 | 28 | 28 to 28 = 1 to 1 |
| 8 | 32 | 36 | 32 to 36 = 8 to 9 |
| 9 | 36 | 45 | 36 to 45 = 4 to 5 |

Page 33.  16   1 + 3 + 5 = 9
          22   1 + 3 + 5 + 7 = 16
          28   1 + 3 + 5 + 7 + 9 = 25

Page 34.

| Long stair | Units of perimeter (P) | Square units of area (A) | Ratio of P to A |
|------------|------------------------|--------------------------|------------------|
| 1 | 4 | 1 | 4 to 1 |
| 2 | 10 | 4 | 10 to 4 = 5 to 2 |
| 3 | 16 | 9 | 16 to 9 |
| 4 | 22 | 16 | 22 to 16 = 11 to 8 |
| 5 | 28 | 25 | 28 to 25 |
| 6 | 34 | 36 | 34 to 36 = 17 to 18 |
| 7 | 40 | 49 | 40 to 49 |
| 8 | 46 | 64 | 46 to 64 = 23 to 32 |
| 9 | 52 | 81 | 52 to 81 |

Page 35.

| Zig-zag | Perimeter | Area |
|---------|-----------|------|
| 1 | 4 | 1 |
| 2 | 12 | 5 |
| 3 | 20 | 13 |

Page 36.

| Zig-zag | Units of perimeter (P) | Square units of area (A) | Ratio of P to A |
|---------|------------------------|--------------------------|------------------|
| 1 | 4 | 1 | 4 to 1 |
| 2 | 12 | 5 | 12 to 5 |
| 3 | 20 | 13 | 20 to 13 |
| 4 | 28 | 25 | 28 to 25 |
| 5 | 36 | 41 | 36 to 41 |
| 6 | 44 | 61 | 44 to 61 |
| 7 | 52 | 85 | 52 to 85 |
| 8 | 60 | 113 | 60 to 113 |

Page 37.

| Moat | Outer Perimeter | Inner Perimeter | Total Perimeter | Area |
|------|-----------------|-----------------|-----------------|------|
| 1 | 12 | 4 | 16 | 8 |
| 2 | 16 | 8 | 24 | 12 |
| 3 | 20 | 12 | 32 | 16 |
| 4 | 24 | 16 | 40 | 20 |

93

Page 38.

| Square moat | Outer perimeter | Inner perimeter | Total perimeter (P) | Area (A) | Ratio of P to A |
|---|---|---|---|---|---|
| 1 | 12 | 4 | 16 | 8 | 16 to 8 = 2 to 1 |
| 2 | 16 | 8 | 24 | 12 | 24 to 12 = 2 to 1 |
| 3 | 20 | 12 | 32 | 16 | 32 to 16 = 2 to 1 |
| 4 | 24 | 16 | 40 | 20 | 40 to 20 = 2 to 1 |
| 5 | 28 | 20 | 48 | 24 | 48 to 24 = 2 to 1 |
| 6 | 32 | 24 | 56 | 28 | 56 to 28 = 2 to 1 |
| 7 | 36 | 28 | 64 | 32 | 64 to 32 = 2 to 1 |
| 8 | 40 | 32 | 72 | 36 | 72 to 36 = 2 to 1 |
| 9 | 44 | 36 | 80 | 40 | 80 to 40 = 2 to 1 |

Page 39.   90 degrees

Page 40.   6 green triangles
$\frac{1}{6}$ of 360° = 60°

6 blue rhombi
$\frac{1}{6}$ of 360° = 60°

6 trapezoids
$\frac{1}{6}$ of 360° = 60°

Page 41.   120 degrees
120 degrees
120 degrees
30 degrees

Page 42.   150°
180°
180°
270°

Page 44.

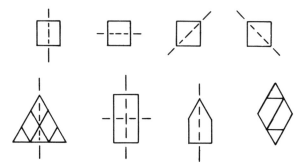

Page 45.   2 lines

1 line

Page 46.   2 lines

Page 47.

This is the only way to get one line of symmetry.

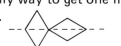

The tan rhombus has the same patterns.

Page 48.   2 lines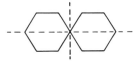

1 line
Any position between the above and

There is always at least one line of symmetry.

Page 49.   1 line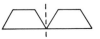

0 lines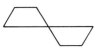

0 lines

1 line

94

Page 50.　lines of symmetry

Page 51.　lines of symmetry

Page 53.　One or two lines of symmetry depending on whether design has been flipped or turned.

Page 54.　lines of symmetry

Page 55.

Page 56.　These are congruent triangles.

Page 57.

They are not congruent.
The sides are congruent except for the long side of the trapezoid.

The small red, the small blue, and the green angle are congruent.
The large red and large blue angles are also congruent.

Page 58.　

Page 58.　Yes, the hexagons are congruent.
The large red and large blue angles are congruent to the angles of the hexagon.
The triangle, small blue rhombus, and small trapezoid angles are congruent.

Page 61.

4 lines of　　　1 line of　　　6 lines of
symmetry　　　symmetry　　　symmetry

square,　triangle,　hexagon

Page 62.　squares only

Page 63.　triangles only

Page 64.

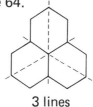 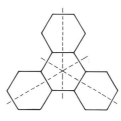

3 lines　　　　　2 lines

 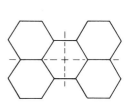

3 lines　　　　　2 lines

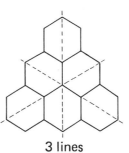 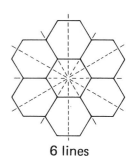

3 lines　　　　　6 lines

95

Page 65. Only triangles and squares will fit.

Page 66. Only 7 hexagons and 12 triangles
will fit correctly.
To extend the pattern each hexagon
should be surrounded with triangles
on the sides and should have corners
touching other hexagons.

Page 70.

| Long name | Short name |
|-----------|-----------|
| 3-3-3-3-3-3 | $3^6$ |
| 6-6-6 | $6^3$ |

Page 71. C

| Figure | Long name | Short name |
|--------|-----------|-----------|
| A | 3-6-3-6 | none |
| B | 3-3-3-3-6 | $3^4$-6 |
| C | 3-4-6-4 | none |
| D | 3-3-4-3-4 | $3^2$-4-3-4 |

Pages 73-82. See page 83.

Page 84.

| Picture | Dimensions | Perimeter | Area |
|---------|-----------|-----------|------|
| | 3 x 5 | 16 | 15 |
| | 4 x 4 | 16 | 16 |

Rules: Perimeter = 2(length + width)
Area = length x width

Page 85.

| Area | Perimeter (P) | No. squares any size | Inner edges (I) | P + I | (P + I) ÷ 4 |
|------|---------------|---------------------|-----------------|-------|-------------|
| 1 | 4 | 1 | 0 | 4 | 1 |
| 4 | 8 | 5 | 4 | 12 | 3 |
| 9 | 12 | 14 | 12 | 24 | 6 |
| 16 | 16 | 30 | 24 | 40 | 10 |

Page 85.

| Fig. | Area (A) | Perimeter (P) | Inner edge (I) | P + I | (P + I) ÷ 4 |
|------|----------|---------------|----------------|-------|-------------|
| | 1 | 4 | 0 | 4 | 1 |
| | 5 | 20 | 0 | 20 | 5 |
| | 13 | 36 | 16 | 52 | 13 |
| 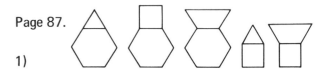 | 25 | 52 | 48 | 100 | 25 |

Page 87.

1)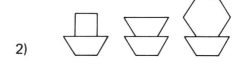

2) 

3)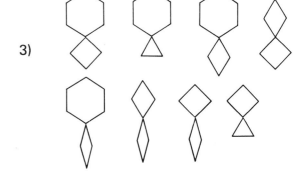

4)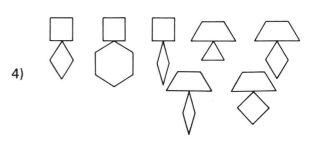

Page 88.

| Picture | Name | Number of sides or angles $n$ | Fewest number of triangles $n-2$ | Total interior degrees $180°(n-2)$ | Measure of interior angle $\frac{180°(n-2)}{n}$ | Measure of central angle $\frac{360°}{n}$ |
|---------|------|---|---|------|------|------|
| | triangle | 3 | 1 | 180° | 60° | 120° |
| | square | 4 | 2 | 360° | 90° | 90° |
| | pentagon | 5 | 3 | 540° | 108° | 72° |
| | hexagon | 6 | 4 | 720° | 120° | 60° |
| | heptagon | 7 | 5 | 900° | $128\frac{4}{7}°$ | $51\frac{3}{7}°$ |
| | octagon | 8 | 6 | 108° | 135° | 45° |

sum is always 180°

96